Granny and the Wild Haggis

This book belongs to

....

By David McNiven Illustrated by Peter McNiven

Layout Design - Mark Bennett

ISBN 978-0-9931688-3-3

Printed by Martins, Berwick-upon-Tweed

Other titles by David McNiven
Me Nan found a leprechaun
Granny and the Loch Ness Monster
Me Nan, Auntie Bridie and the leprechaun

To the haggis Rabbie Burns wrote:
You've "an honest sonsie face."
In the next line he said that haggis
Is, "chieftain of the pudding-race."

But did you ever see a haggis,
In the butchers on a tray?
And wonder, "Does he shoot them?
Or does he catch them far away?"

My Grandpa says they live up north,
In those hills near Aberdeen
And in bonnie glens at sunset,
They come down
to wash and preen.

Uncle Billy says they've got three legs!
And you can pick them up in sacks,
Because they run around in circles,
Then fall over on their backs.

Or run round hills ANTICLOCKWISE,

Until they climb up to the peak,

They roll back down to the bottom

And lie there in a dizzy heap!!

They've a hooley every Friday night,
You can hear their whoops and squeals.
But because they **don't** turn clockwise,
They **don't** dance eightsome reels.

Here in Scotland every August
They shoot grouse and it's a bird.
Could the haggis be a bird as well?
Or is that idea absurd?

They're in our fish 'n' chip shop,
So maybe it's a fish?
With chips and crispy batter,
Now there's a tasty dish.

DID SOME ONE
SAY RABBIT

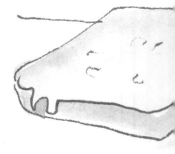

They eat HAMburgers in America,
But they're all made with BEEF.
And a HOT DOG is a roll and sausage,
So for all dogs that's a relief.

In Wales they eat Welsh rabbit,
But that's just cheese on toast!
But in Scotland we eat haggis,
Boiled or fried, or even roast.

But Gran says that's all nonsense,
You know haggis tastes so nice.
It's made with minced lamb and liver,
Oatmeal, onions and some spice.

We Scots love eating haggis,
We bought one for our dinner.
At our butchers on the corner,
Their haggis is a winner.

Gran put the haggis on the cooker
With some onions in a pot,
With hot water and some vegetables,
Then she boiled up the lot.

Gran left it there to simmer,
For an hour or two to cook,
But then she heard such a commotion,
She ran back in to have a look.

HELP MA BOB!

She lifted up the lid of the pot,
And found to her dismay,
Our haggis had eaten the onion and veg,
And was singing

SCOTS WHA HAE

But then the haggis turned around!!
Snarled and gave an evil chuckle,
The haggis grabbed the lid of the pot,
And *whacked* her on the knuckle!!

Gran jumped back shrieking with the pain
And called for us to come,
We thought that it was all a joke
And ran in to join the fun.

EEEK
MICHTY
ME

GASP

GASP

But then we both just stood and gasped,
Because we had never seen
A huge haggis climbing out of the pot,
With

THREE LITTLE LEGS OF GREEN

He waddled across the marble top
And gave a vicious snarl,
Then he ate all of our biscuits!
Then ate the biscuit barrel!

YUM

CHOMP

CHOMP

Strawb

He next ate four bananas,
Then three apples and a pear,
Two plums and a lovely nectarine,
And whatever else was there.

He bit a chunk out
of the chopping board,
Shrieked and gave a R O A R,
Then turned round in a circle
And jumped down on the floor.

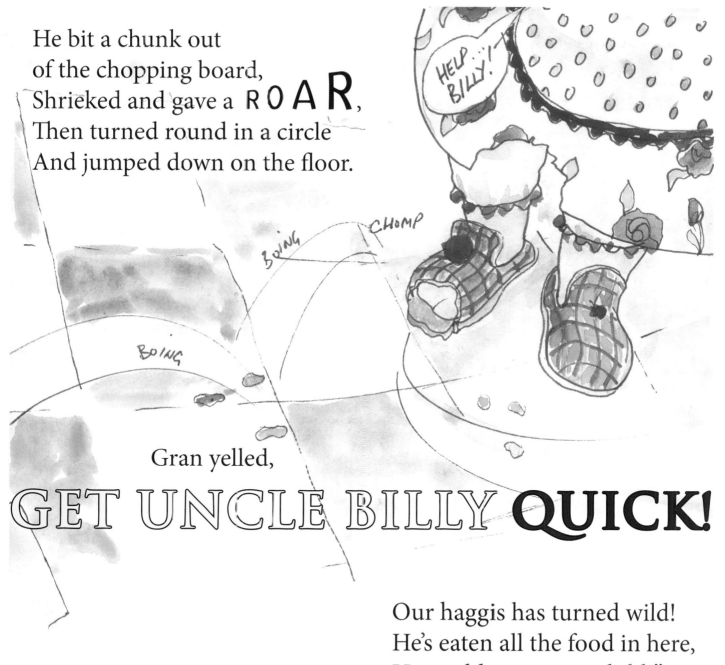

Gran yelled,

GET UNCLE BILLY QUICK!

Our haggis has turned wild!
He's eaten all the food in here,
He could even eat a child!"

He ran circles round poor Granny,
Then rolled over on his back,

So our Uncle Billy grabbed him,
And stuffed him in a sack!!!

Now I never believed my Grandpa
About the hills near Aberdeen,
Those stories that he told me
About them coming down to preen.

As for Uncle Billy's nonsense
About them rolling on their backs,
How you could go and pick them up,
And then put them into sacks?

IN YE POP

I always thought my Gran was right
And Gran knew what was best,
But I saw those little legs of green,
I never would have guessed.

So I still have to wonder
When I see a haggis on a tray,
Does he make them? does he shoot them?
Or does he catch them far away…?

Some Haggis Facts

When the Romans invaded Scotland, very few of them ever saw a haggis. They therefore called it *Haggis Neversaurus*.

The few who did see a haggis but never caught one called it *Haggis Nevercaughtus*.

Much later when the Scots peasants had hunted the haggis to near extinction, they decided to make their own haggis.

At this time the controlling landlords kept all the animals in Scotland for eating themselves and the peasants were starving.

One starving clever peasant took all the bits of sheep the landowners would not eat and chopped them up with some vegetables and some oatmeal and herbs and cooked it.

…And with a few recipe changes he invented the HAGGIS!